American Folk Songs for CHRISTMAS

by Ruth Crawford Seeger

ILLUSTRATED BY BARBARA COONEY

Doubleday & Company, Inc. Garden City, New York

Of the fifty-five songs and one fiddle tune in this book, thirteen were notated from recordings of traditional singing and playing made by folklorists and deposited in the Archive of American Folk Song in the Library of Congress in Washington. One was notated from a commercial recording of a folk singer, one direct from the singer. Eight were found in shape-note books and the remainder in folklore journals and collections.

The book had its beginning in 1945 at the Whitehall Country School of Bethesda, Maryland. Soon after Thanksgiving the English instructor used to turn her eighth-grade class loose in the Bible. Their assignment was the finding of verses which, alternating with music, would tell the Christmas story at the brief Christmas program. The story was thus put together afresh each year, and songs were chosen according to its needs. The Bible verses were spoken chiefly by the upper grades; younger grades had occasional lines. During my two years at the school American folk songs were sung on these programs, either unaccompanied or with autoharp, dulcimer, or guitar. No piano was used.

Best liked by the younger children were the shorter songs from oral tradition, such as *Mary Had a Baby; Sing Hallelu; Oh, Watch the Stars; Jesus Borned in Bethlea; Ain't That a Rocking All Night*, etc. Older grades sang the shape-note songs with an enthusiasm equal to that which still draws whole families from miles around, in many parts of the South, for two or three days of continuous singing from shape-note books. The famous "shape" or "patent" notes were invented over 150 years ago to facilitate note-reading of hymns, and have since been widely used in North, South, and West. Shape-note singers read the degrees of the scale of the shape of the note-heads rather than by their location on lines or spaces. Some systems use four shapes, some seven — as, for instance:

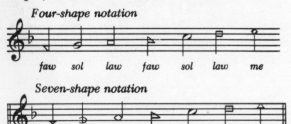

Four-shape notation

faw sol law faw sol law me

Seven-shape notation

do ra mi fa sol la si

The piano accompaniments to *A Virgin Most Pure; Shepherds, Rejoice; Star in the East*, and *Babe of Bethlehem* are exact condensations of the original shape-note settings. Accompaniments to *Awake; Exultation; Children of the Heavenly King*, and *Rejoice My Friends* are simplifications of the settings: to permit playing on the piano at proper speed, some tones have been omitted but none added. The accompaniment to *Cradle Hymn* is based on the shape-note setting of the closely related *Restoration*. In all accompaniments the tune (originally in the middle or tenor part) has been placed "on top" — an inversion not foreign to oral usage, which occasionally turns written intervals upside down (see page 9).

Chord letters have been placed above the staff line of each song, chiefly for use in accompaniment by such instruments as autoharp, guitar, or banjo. Many of the songs sound better without any accompaniment at all. A metronome mark has been given for each song. Parentheses around a metronome mark indicate that there was none in the original source and that the speed has been estimated.

There have been many contributors to this collection. First, the singers. Next, the collectors who recorded their singing: John A. and Alan Lomax, Herbert Halpert, Sidney Robertson Cowell, and Alton C. Morris. Then Kate Duvall Pitts, Kathleen M. Thorne, and Rachel Hall of Whitehall School, who were first to urge that the Christmas songs we were singing be made more widely available. At the Library of Congress Rae Korson, Reference Librarian of the Archive, gave extensive assistance, and Frank Campbell and Oliver Dudley of the Music Division went out of their way to help. Through his several volumes George Pullen Jackson was a silently eloquent consultant, and Irving and Violet Lowens answered frequent questions about shape-note songs. Robert Winslow Gordon sang for me. Glenore Horne gave many valuable thoughts and hours. Esther Williamson Ballou, Sidney Cowell, and Vanett Lawler assisted with music proof and Introduction. My husband, Charles Seeger, and

our children, Michael, Margaret, Barbara, and Penelope, are constant contributors in patience, encouragement, ideas, and work to anything I do.

Acknowledgment is due also to the publishers, societies, institutions, and individuals mentioned in the following page-by-page list of sources. Pages and song titles are in **heavy type.** Key letters are used for sources quoted more than once:

AAFS: *Archive of American Folk Song,* Folklore Section, Library of Congress, Washington, D.C.

BWS: *Befo' de War Spirituals,* by E. A. McIlhenny, copyright, 1933, by E. A. McIlhenny, Christopher Publishing House, Boston.

CPS: *Calhoun Plantation Songs,* by Emily Hallowell, copyright, 1907, by Emily Hallowell, C. W. Thompson and Co., Boston.

DES: *Down-East Spirituals,* by George Pullen Jackson, J. J. Augustin, New York, 1941.

FSA: *Folk-Songs of America,* by Robert W. Gordon, copyright, 1927–28, by the New York Times. Reprinted, 1938, by the National Service Bureau, Federal Theater Project of the Works Progress Administration, New York.

GTBS: *The Gift to Be Simple,* by Edward D. Andrews, copyright, 1940, by Edward D. Andrews, J. J. Augustin, New York.

JAFL: *Journal of American Folklore,* The American Folklore Society.

MEL: *Mellows,* by R. Emmett Kennedy, copyright, 1925, by Albert and Charles Boni, New York.

RFSN: *Religious Folk Songs of the Negro, As Sung on the Plantations,* ed. by Thomas P. Fenner, copyright, 1909, by Hampton Normal and Agricultural Institute, Hampton, Va.

SNS: *Seventy Negro Spirituals,* by William Arms Fisher, copyright, 1926, by Oliver Ditson Co., Boston.

SOH: *The Southern Harmony,* compiled by William Walker, E. W. Miller, Philadelphia, 1854. Reprint by Hastings House, New York, 1939.

SOM: *The Southern Minstrel,* compiled by L. J. Jones, Philadelphia, 1849.

SSUS: *Slave Songs of the United States,* by William Francis Allen, Charles Pickard Ware, and Lucy McKim Garrison, copyright, 1867, by A. Simpson and Co., New York. Reprint by Peter Smith, New York, 1929.

STHIS: *St. Helena Island Spirituals,* by N. G. J. Ballanta-Taylor, copyright, 1925, by Penn Normal, Industrial and Agricultural School, St. Helena Island, S.C. (Press of G. Schirmer.)

Pages 8, 9, 10. In the Morning When I Rise, from SSUS, p. 15. **South Carolina Watch Night Service,** see *A Plantation Christmas,* by Julia Peterkin, 1929 and 1934, Houghton Mifflin Co., The Riverside Press, Cambridge. **Georgia Watch Night Service,** see FSA, pp. 30–32. **Sweep, Sweep and Cleanse Your Floor,** and other Shaker data, from GTBS, pp. 9, 28, 32, 35–37, 125. Other sources: *Poems,* by Irwin Russell, New York, 1888, "Christmas Night in the Quarters," pp. 1–10. JAFL, Vol. 9, 1896, p. 178, "Christmas Maskings in Boston," by W. W. Newell. *Social Life in Old New England,* by Mary Caroline Crawford, Boston, 1914, p. 501. *Recollections of Samuel Breck,* ed. by H. W. Scudder, Philadelphia, 1877, pp. 35–36. *The Ozarks,* by Vance Randolph, New York, 1931, p. 65. *Devil's Ditties,* by Jean Thomas, Chicago, 1931, pp. 15–18. *Ballad Makin' in the Kentucky Mountains,* by Jean Thomas, New York, 1939, p. 225. *The Frank C. Brown Collection of North Carolina Folklore,* Duke University Press, Durham, N.C., 1952, Vol. 1, pp. 239–41. *The Pennsylvania German Folklore Society,* Vol. VI, pp. 15–22, "Twelvetide," by Edwin M. Fogel. *Our Southern Highlanders,* by Horace Kephart, The Outing Publishing Co., 1913, The Macmillan Co., 1922, p. 340. *Southern Folklore Quarterly,* Vol. 11, pp. 237–39, "The New Year's Shoot," by Arthur Palmer Hudson. *Publications of the Texas Folk-lore Society,* Vol. 5, pp. 109–11, "Pioneer Christmas Customs of Tarrant County," by Mary Daggett Lake. *Southern Workman,* Vol. 37, pp. 686–89, "Christmas in Virginia before the War," by Florence Whiting Lee. **Page 12. Stars in the Heaven** (part of "Gospel Train"), from BWS, p. 107. **Page 13. Oh, Watch the Stars,** from STHIS,

p. 58. **Page 14. Great Big Stars** ("Shine, Shine"), song and st. 1 from *The Story of the Jubilee Singers*, ed. by J. B. I. Marsh, Hodder and Stoughton, London, 1877, p. 220; st. 2 improvised. **Shine Like a Star in the Morning** (refrain only), from AAFS 46 B, Album 10. **Page 15. Bright Morning Stars Are Rising,** from AAFS 1379 A1. The term "shouting" can refer to one of various forms of religious dance, usually with clapping and singing. Or it can have vocal meaning only. There are occasional Biblical references to shouting in worship, such as "O clap your hands, all ye people; shout unto God with the voice of triumph" (Psalms 47:1). **Page 16. Rise Up, Shepherd, and Follow,** from RFSN, p. 173. **Page 18. Shepherd, Shepherd,** from *American Negro Songs*, by John W. Work, copyright, 1940, by John W. Work, Theodore Presser Co., Philadelphia, p. 68. **Page 19. Don't You Hear the Lambs a-Crying?,** from AAFS 917 A2. **Page 20. Found My Lost Sheep,** from CPS, p. 10. **Page 21. Look Away to Bethlehem,** tune (rhythm edited) and st. 1 from *A Collection of Revival Hymns and Plantation Melodies*, by Marshall W. Taylor, Taylor and Echols, Cincinnati, 1882, p. 160; st. 2, from JAFL, Vol. 40, 1927, pp. 214–303, "Negro Folk Tales from the South," by Arthur Huff Fauset. **Page 22. How Many Miles to Beth-e-le-hem?,** chant from AAFS 2959 A2 and 3051 A3; song from *Folk Songs of Old New England*, by Eloise H. Linscott, copyright, 1939, by The Macmillan Co., New York, p. 18. See also *The Traditional Games of England, Scotland and Ireland*, by Alice Bertha Gomme, Vol. 1, pp. 231–38. **Page 23. Jehovah Hallelujah,** from SSUS, p. 2 (tune edited). **Page 24. Joseph and Mary,** song and fiddle tune from AAFS 1010 A1. **Page 26. A Virgin Most Pure** ("Virgin Unspotted"), tune and st. 1–4 from DES p. 26, quoted from a MS 4-shape song book made near Emmitsburg, Md., between 1800 and 1830; st. 5 and accompaniment from *Repository of Sacred Music, Part Second*, by John Wyeth, Harrisburg, Pa., 1820, p. 79. **Page 28. Baby Born Today,** tune from Robert W. Gordon as learned from Mary Mann, Darien, Ga., 1926; text and note from FSA, pp. 30–32. **Page 29. Go Tell It on the Mountain,** from RFSN, p. 174. **Page 30. Shepherds, Rejoice,** from shape-note book *The Social Harp*, by John G. McCurry, S. C. Collins, Philadelphia, 1868, p. 78. **Page 32. Shepherds in Judea** ("As Shepherds in Jewry") tune and st. 2–4 (slightly

edited) from DES, p. 65, quoted from *The Christian Harmony or Songster's Companion,* compiled by Jeremiah Ingalls, Exeter, N. H., 1805. For st. 1, see *Some Ancient Christmas Carols*, by Davies Gilbert, London, 1823, p. 11. **Page 34. The New-Born Baby,** from SNS, p. 24. This song was heard from fishermen leaving the Charleston harbor on their way to the fishing banks. **Page 35. Oh, Mary and the Baby, Sweet Lamb** ("Mary and the Baby"), from AAFS 913 B2. **Page 36. Star in the East,** from shape-note book SOH, p. 16 (original setting slightly edited: E-flat omitted above the tune in meas. 6, 17, 21, 30). **Page 38. Babe of Bethlehem,** from shape-note book SOH, p. 78 (st. 1 edited). **Page 40. Child of God,** tune and st. 1 from MEL, p. 45. Used by permission. St. 2–5, from JAFL, Vol. 12, 1899, p. 272, "Christmas Carols in Georgia," by Emma Backus. (These, published in JAFL without a tune, have been slightly adapted.) **Page 41. Cradle Hymn,** from *Devil's Ditties*, by Jean Thomas (The Traipsin' Woman) copyright, 1931, by W. Wilbur Hatfield, Chicago, p. 119. The tune, from a Tennessee singer, is closely related to the shape-note "Restoration" (SOH; p. 5), whose 3-part setting has been used as basis for the piano accompaniment. The words are part of the 14-stanza poem by Isaac Watts. In Kentucky, "Cradle Hymn" stanzas are said to have been sung to the tune of "Go Tell Aunt Nancy." This latter can be found as "Greenville" in the 1823 edition of *The Handel and Haydn Society Collection of Church Music*, p. 233. And "Greenville" appears to be a simplification of an air from Jean Jacques Rousseau's opera *Le Devin du Village*, first performed at Fontainebleau in 1752. Rousseau's tune is itself clearly in folk idiom. **Page 42. Ain't That a Rocking All Night,** from STHIS, p. 5. **Page 43. Sing-a-Lamb,** tune ("Black Betty") from AAFS 200 B2 and 205 A2; text from *Ole Time Religion*, by Mary Belle McKellar, published by El Karubah Temple, Shreveport, La., 1927. Spiritual and work songs are often interrelated. This fragmentary religious text, with no tune, is set to that of a work song with such patently similar lines as "Black Betty had a baby, bam-ba-lam." **Page 44. Mary, What You Going to Name That Pretty Little Baby?,** from *African Music in America*, by Jeanette Robinson Murphy, The Bandanna Publishing Co., New York, 1904, p. 33 (slightly edited). **Page 46. Sing Hallelu,** from STHIS, p. 41 (tune edited). **Page 47. Mary Had a Baby,** from STHIS, p. 40.

Page 48. Jesus Borned in Bethlea, from AAFS 3160 A1 (see also *American Folk Songs for Children*, by Ruth Crawford Seeger, Doubleday and Co., New York, 1948). **Page 49. Wasn't That a Mighty Day,** tune and refrain from STHIS, p. 51; stanza from JAFL, Vol. 27, 1914, p. 264, "Some Negro Folk Songs from Tennessee," by Anna Franz Odum. The latter begins "David was a baby," ends "The beefsteak keep-a him warm." Confusing of David with Jesus is not surprising, as he is also a favorite Bible figure among folk singers. But beefsteak was puzzling until a stanza appeared in Taylor's *A Collection of Revival Hymns and Plantation Melodies* (p. 21), ending "And the beasts did keep him warm." **Page 50. January, February** ("The Last Month of the Year"), from AAFS 3087 B2. **Page 52. Poor Little Jesus,** from *Folksong USA*, by John A. and Alan Lomax, Charles and Ruth Seeger, Music Editors, Duell, Sloane and Pearce, New York, 1947, p. 354. **Page 53. Heard from Heaven Today,** from SSUS, p. 20. **Page 54. 'Twas a Wonder in Heaven** ("Bye and Bye"), from CPS, p. 60. **Page 55. Mariner's Hymn,** from DES, p. 254, quoted from *The Milennial Harp*, compiled by Joshua V. Himes, Boston, 1843, ii, p. 39. **Page 56. O Mary, Where Is Your Baby?,** from MEL, p. 74. Used by permission. **Page 57. Yonder Comes Sister Mary,** from SNS, p. 208. **Page 58. The Blessings of Mary,** tune and st. 1–10 (two of these slightly edited) from JAFL, Vol. 48, p. 390, coll. by Richard Chase; st. 11–12, from DES, p. 63. **Page 60. Awake** ("Loving Kindness"), tune and st. 1 from shape-note book *The Sacred Harp*, by B. F. White and E. J. King, published by S. C. Collins, Philadelphia, 1870, p. 275; st. 2, from J. Dobell's *New Selections*, 1806; st. 3, composited. **Page 61. Exultation,** from shape-note book SOH, p. 88. **Page 62. Children of the Heavenly King** ("Mercer"), from shape-note book SOM, p. 67. **Page 64. Singing in the Land,** from CPS, p. 37. **Page 65. Rejoice My Friends** ("Knoxville"), from SOM, p. 172. **Page 66. The Twelve Apostles,** from AAFS 4087 A and B, sung by Ivalee Hobden. Comparison of a dozen American versions from Kentucky, North Carolina, Massachusetts, New York State, and Arkansas yields interesting number variants. Number nine, for instance: the moonshine bright and clear, the nine bright lights a-shining, the sunshines bright and fair, both bright and shiny. Eight: the eight Archangels, captain angels, royal martyrs, Gabriel angels. Seven is usually about stars. Six: the single weavers, the

cheerful waiters, the charming waiters, the bold waiters, the broad waters. Five: flamboys *(flambeaux?)* under the bough, ferrymen in the boat, farmers in a boat, fingers on the bow, tumblers on a board. Four varies little from gospel writers or preachers (occasionally teachers). Three may be divers, drivers, shrivers, riders, strangers. See also JAFL, Vol. 4, 1891, p. 216, "The Carol of the Numbers," by W. W. Newell. **Page 69. Little Bitty Baby,** from *The Swapping Song Book*, by Jean Ritchie, Oxford University Press, New York, 1952, p. 86. **Page 70. Holy Babe,** from AAFS 49 A and B, Album 10. **Page 72. The Twelve Days of Christmas,** from AAFS 989 A1. See also *Folksongs of Florida*, by Alton C. Morris, University of Florida Press, Gainesville, p. 416. For game directions, see *Folk Songs of Old New England* (cited above), p. 52. **Page 74. The Angel Band** ("Band of Angels"), from *Thirty-Six South Carolina Spirituals*, by Carl Diton, copyright, 1930, by G. Schirmer, Inc., New York, p. 30. Reprinted by permission. See also *The Negro and His Songs*, by Howard W. Odum and Guy B. Johnson, p. 104. **Page 76. Almost Day** ("Christmas Song"), from *Play-Parties in Song and Dance*, by Leadbelly (Huddie Ledbetter), Asch Album SC, record SC-34X. By permission of Folkways Music Publishers, Inc., New York. For "Looka Day," see FSA, p. 30. **Page 77. Heaven Bell Ring,** from SSUS, p. 20. **Page 78. A Mince Pie or a Pudding,** from GTBS, p. 130. **Page 79. Christmas Day in the Morning** ("Sunny Bank"), from DES, p. 63, quoted from University of Virginia MS Collection of Folk-Music, No. 183; st. 6 and 8 from *Folk Songs du Midi des Etats-Unis*, by Josiah H. Combs, Les Presses Universitaires de France, Paris, 1925, p. 163. New York text from JAFL, Vol. 5, 1892, p. 326, "Old English Songs in American Versions," by W. W. Newell. **Page 80. Old Christmas** (fiddle tune), from AAFS 1503 B1. A story from Texas illustrates two characteristics of folk singing and playing — the improvising and the insistent keeping-going. A fiddler's house caught fire while he was singing and playing *The Arkansas Traveller*. "Amid all the excitement . . . Uncle Jack went right on fiddling. When told of the fire, in place of the line 'Why don't you play the rest of the tune?' he improvised 'Boys, please go put it out,' and continued playing his piece. When asked afterward why he didn't stop and help put the fire out, he replied, 'Dang it, I was in a place where I couldn't stop.'"

Alphabetical Song Contents

Contents

Introduction

Here are Christmas songs, and songs for Christmas, from American English-speaking folk tradition. Most of them are truly Christmas songs. Some have only occasional Christmas lines or stanzas. And some are, strictly speaking, not songs of Christmas at all, but songs related to it in mood or subject — prelude of stars, shepherds, and sheep, and postlude of praise, worship, and festivity. These latter are included in a Christmas book because, during my work at schools with children of varying ages, I have found that such songs fill a need at Christmas time. They provide a frame for the Christmas picture, a path to and from the scene of the drama. Some were chosen by the children themselves for specific uses in the programs they were planning.

The book has been so arranged as to tell the Christmas story step by step, from song to song. After preliminary setting of the stage the drama begins — the looking away to Bethlehem, wondering how far it is, the unborn Baby foretelling His birthday (*Joseph and Mary*), the journey to Jerusalem (*A Virgin Most Pure*) — and no place for the Son of God to lay His head (*Jehovah Hallelujah*). The Child is born (*The New-Born Baby*) and there is great rejoicing (*Go Tell It on the Mountains; Shepherds, Rejoice*). His ancestry is traced and the story told in detail (*Babe of Bethlehem*). Shepherds arrive, presents are given (*Shepherds in Judea; Star in the East*). The Child is rocked (*Ain't That a Rocking All Night*), sung to (*Sing-a-Lamb*), named (*Mary, What You Going to Name That Pretty Little Baby?*), worshiped (*'Twas a Wonder in Heaven*), affectionately sympathized with (*Poor Little Jesus*). He grows up (*O Mary, Where Is Your Baby?*) and Mary is proud of Him (*The Blessings of Mary*). Finally, out of His greatness come many kinds of singing: music of religious praise (*Awake; Children of the Heavenly King; Rejoice My Friends*) and music more generally festive.

These songs grew out of and were used in the old-time American Christmas, a Christmas not of Santa Claus and tinseled trees but of homespun worship and festivity. ("Old-time" music is a folk name for folk music.) They have been chosen for their excellence as songs but even more for the genuineness with which they express the Christmas attitudes and values of the people who sang them and the communities of which they were part. Some have come down, singer to singer, for generations; others are local, home-grown. Some are from oral (folk) tradition; others are of mixed oral and written origin. Some are gentle, rich in poetic fantasy; others are of austere strength. Some are free, improvisational; others, more set in text and tune.

Many are of the nature of folk carols. They are direct expressions from everyday people. In them the singer extends toward Deity the same intimate neighborliness which inclines him on other days of the year to greet his God with:

They are fresh, rhythmically buoyant: singing them, it is easy to remember that clapping, foot tapping, and religious dancing have been their frequent accompaniment. They are simple and without pretense. They exist because there was need for them. A considerable number — the response songs, particularly — stem from vigorous traditions of group spontaneity in singing, work, and worship.

This group spontaneity is nowhere more evident than at an all-night Watch Night service in a small church on Christmas Eve. Song and sermon and prayer flow back and forth with little break from one to the other. Leader and group are joint worshipers and makers of song. A short phrase of music and a brief refrain fill long spaces of night, with each minute detail of the Christmas story lined out — new lines improvised, old lines remembered.

The Watch Night service in a South Carolina meetinghouse began after early supper and ceased only when the Christmas star was well up in the sky on Christmas morning. (At home the cows had been left unmilked with their calves, because all mothers want to be with their children at midnight on Christmas Eve.) Singing was solemn until midnight, when the awaited crowing of the cock proclaimed the holy hour. (Some say roosters crow at midnight only on Christmas Eve.) At this signal the mood changed, speed increased, and "shouts" were begun. A shout is a song usually with short lines and short refrain, often accompanied by clapping and a sort of shuffling dance called "shouting." Specific rules, such as the ban on crossing of feet, distinguished the "holy dance" from "sinful" or everyday dancing, and a watchman was frequently appointed to see that feet obeyed.

In a little church in Georgia it was the watchman's added duty to watch for the rising of the star. He first went out to look for it soon after midnight. *Looka Day* was sung about that time, and returned to again and again through the night, interspersed with other shouts and spirituals (among them, *The Twelve Blessings of Mary*). At last the Christmas star was announced, and there was a song about it.

> Thought I heard Father Johnny say
> Call the nation great and small
> Look up the road at thy right hand
> The star give its light.

Then came the shout *Baby Born Today*, sung back and forth from leader to group for a long time. Finally day was "broad clear" and the watchman must begin the closing song. If the group was not ready to go home, a good-natured tussle followed:

the watchman's mouth was covered with handkerchiefs to stop his song, he was led outside, guards were set to keep him — and the singing continued on into morning.

On a borderline between folk music and hymn are many of the songs in shape-note books. In these songs, as in some of the traditional Christmas songs of other countries, literary texts are set to tunes whose folk character is obvious. (See pages 2–5.)

Some of the finest of the shape-note books, and those richest in folk material, were compiled by men who traveled as itinerant singing teachers throughout rural areas. They would put up at local homes, gather people together for a week or two of strenuous singing school, sell their favorite books — and move on. No wonder some shape-note tunes show folk influence! It would be strange if, living among singing people and hearing the dance songs and banjo and fiddle tunes and love songs and ballads all around, these singing editors had not written down some of the secular folk tunes for religious use. The strands of oral song are well tangled!

In shape-note books the songs are arranged for either three or four voice parts. The three-part settings are most distinctive, though four parts are now favored. In the former the melody is carried in the middle part by the high men's voices (tenor). Above the tenor is a treble or descant (soprano) and below it the bass. However, women sometimes join in the tenor part (an octave higher than written) and men in the treble (an octave or two lower). Harmonies are sparse, often stern and bare, occasionally dissonant — as shown in the shape-note piano accompaniments in this book, which are either condensations or simplifications of the original vocal settings (see page 2). Many shape-note settings show characteristics common to certain medieval music and to some contemporary writing as well.

Not all the songs at Christmas services are Christmas songs. Praise and worship are the general theme: the Christmas story gives it particular and very special meaning. Christmas meetings of the Shaker sect in New England and New York State provide extreme example. Singing, dance, and movement were essential to Shaker worship. Christmas was a day cherished for religious celebration, and song was indispensable to it. Yet there is scarcely any mention of Christmas among available Shaker songs, many of which are close to oral and shape-note traditions.

In one community, on Christmas morning, songs called "gift songs" or "vision songs" awakened the members an hour earlier than usual, a march was sung as they filed into the meetinghouse, and — after simple telling of the Christmas story — many other sings mingled with the elaborate ritual attending the bestowing of "spiritual presents." In another community the Christmas worshipers sang songs as they sat on "carpets of Mother's love, soft as velvet." (Mother Ann Lee was the head of the Shaker sect in this country.) In still another, "sweeping songs" were sung to the rhythm of sweeping and brushing the meeting rooms with brooms received from the spirits.

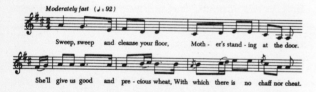

Moderately fast (♩ = 92)

Sweep, sweep and cleanse your floor, Moth-er's stand-ing at the door.
She'll give us good and pre-cious wheat, With which there is no chaff nor cheat.

There has been widespread and heated dispute in American folk tradition about "New Christmas" (December 25) and "Old Christmas" (January 6), as to which of these boundaries of the twelve days was the "real Christmas." Numerous time-honored proofs have been cited in favor of the latter. Only on Old Christmas at midnight does water turn to wine ("Our well had a charm put on it the night the cows talked, and I wouldn't clean it out for silver!"). Only on Old Christmas at sunrise can you see the elderberry sprouting through the hard, frozen ground under the snow ("It's a sign that Old Christmas is the real Christmas, for a fact!"). Bees always buz loud exactly at midnight on Old Christmas Eve, and if several bee gums are together you can hear the "Old Christmas hum" some distance away. ("This shows January 6, not December 25, is the real Christmas.") Children who never heard of Santa Claus, and had little notion of the Christmas story, did know for certain that the beasts,

the cows, and the horses talk to each other at midnight of Old Christmas, and kneel and bellow and make "just the masterest moanin'." Some people say the critters have the gift of speech so they may pray aloud in English. Some say they lift their heads when they pray; others, that they get down on their knees and turn their heads to the east. Still others say that on the night of Old Christmas all the cattle and horses everywhere get up and lie down on the other side. ("That's the sign it is for a fact the good Lord's birth night.")

Christmas is a season of two moods: holy day and holiday. Some pray — and some dance. There is worship — and there is festivity. And in both there is music. The banjo was not allowed at Christmas Eve Watch Night service. But on Christmas night it could join the fiddle in lively sinful tunes (any song whose words were not religious was sinful) and it could keep people dancing all night (with no ban on crossed feet) until the cock crowed at his usual hour of sunrise and it was time to go home — maybe shoes in hand through muddy bottomlands, or four a-straddle a mule, or forty in a ten-ox wagon.

Accounts of traditional American Christmas in its festive mood are scattered and various. Typical of New England until late nineteenth century, perhaps, is the story of Christmas morning around 1800 in the Boston Latin School: the headmaster asked the boys what day it was, and no one knew. Puritan belief vigorously objected to Christmas celebration, but frowned less on the festive than the religious. A Connecticut law banned both, forbidding "reading of Common Prayer, keeping Christmas or saints' days, making minced pies, dancing, playing cards or performing on any instrument, except the drums, trumpet and Jew's-harp"!

There were occasional survivals of the old custom of "mumming." In eighteenth-century Boston, boys and men (sometimes masked, usually wearing outlandish costumes) roamed the streets, gained admission to homes, presented parts of old folk plays, and demanded money or food. More recent accounts from South and West tell of serenaders, usually boys and men, going from house to house on Christmas

Eve or during the twelve-day season, sometimes marching around each house two or three times, singing, ringing cowbells, pounding pans with corncobs, shouting — until finally the door opened, and inside there were warmth and refreshment of apples, cake, dried nuts, cider — and, perhaps, more singing. In a North Carolina town there is a "Speech Crier" who still, every New Year's Eve, chants a traditional poem or "speech" which he learned in 1889 from his older brothers while picking cotton. Beginning at midnight, the speech is recited in front of houses for miles around, followed each time by blasts from a score of hundred-year-old muskets — then silence — and the inevitable invitation to food and drink. This goes on, house to house, for eighteen hours.

Fireworks have long been part of American Christmas, especially in sections of South and West. On Christmas Eve in an Ozark town merchants would donate gunpowder, and the blacksmith would "fire anvils" with terrific racket until about midnight, when it was time for the serenaders to set out. Older reports from Texas and Virginia tell of holes bored in logs and gunpowder poured in — touched off, then, with a pocketknife and a piece of punk. Sometimes boys rolled their mothers' carpet rags into balls, soaked them in oil, lit them, and threw them into the air. Or hog bladders were blown up and dried, to be burst on Christmas morning as substitute for guns. (A hundred years later, boys and men in the Appalachians were shooting off revolvers because they had no firecrackers!)

In gentle contrast to such uproariousness, Christmas in a county of pioneer Texas, as in many other places, was occasion for community festivity, with plenty of singing, dancing, and fiddling. Several weeks before Christmas there were wagon trips to town for luxuries such as sugar and coffee. There were all-night wild-turkey shoots, hunts for possum and coon, and once in a while a bee tree discovered. There were candy pulls, corn poppings, domino and card playing. There was dancing (with fiddle accompaniment, and sometimes harmonica), and there were play-parties (at which the dancing could be accompanied by singing only, because some disapproved of instruments as sinful). Refreshments were usually eggnog, nuts, and coffee, with special treats of clove-scented apple dumplings or rich mince pies.

At the large country houses, Christmas was of course a season busy with parties, visiting, feasting, singing, and dancing — for owners, and usually for servants. Sometimes no work was required for as long as a yule log kept burning (there are tales of thorough soaking in the creek before delivering the log to the master's hearth).

The yule log was not, however, a typical element in rural celebration. Holly is mentioned rarely. As for Santa Claus and the Christmas tree, they are fairly recent importations and not part of old-time American Christmas, (When finally at the "Big House" there was a Christmas tree, it was likely to be trimmed with red apples, homemade cornucopias of bright paper, bags of candy, cookies with colored icing, and bits of raw cotton for snow.) Children occasionally hung stockings and found nuts and apples in them next morning. Exchange of gifts was rare, except for the old custom in which the first to cry "Christmas gift," when two met, must receive a gift from the other.

In this country our modern Christmas has been celebrated to a large extent, with songs gathered by other countries from their respective traditions. This is partly because we have not been aware of our own. They have been hidden away, hard to find, or crowded out by the more easily available published collections around us.

To make more easily available some of these songs from American traditional Christmas, religious and festive, is to serve two ends: to give back to the people songs that belong to them, and to supplement the already rich international store of traditional Christmas song.

Stars in the Heaven

BYE AND BYE

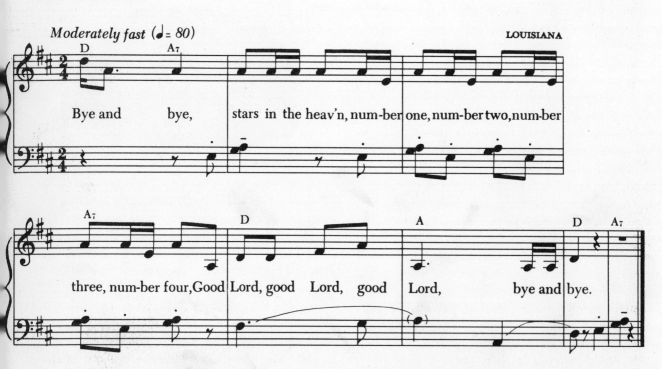

Moderately fast (♩ = 80)   LOUISIANA

Bye and bye, stars in the heav'n, num-ber one, num-ber two, num-ber

three, num-ber four, Good Lord, good Lord, good Lord, bye and bye.

The number of stars may continue far above four — number five,
number six, number seven, and on.

Oh, Watch the Stars

SOUTH CAROLINA

Moderately slow (♩ = 84)

Oh, watch the stars, see how they run, Oh,

watch the stars, see how they run, _____ The_____

stars run down_____ at the set-ting of the sun, Oh,

watch the stars, see how they run.

smooth

13

Great Big Stars

SHINE, SHINE

2. Star in the east, 'way up yonder, *etc.*

Shine Like a Star in the Morning

VIRGINIA

Bright Morning Stars Are Rising

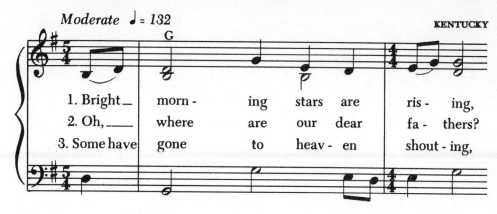

Moderate ♩ = 132

KENTUCKY

1. Bright morn - ing stars are ris - ing,
2. Oh, where are our dear fa - thers?
3. Some have gone to heav - en shout - ing,

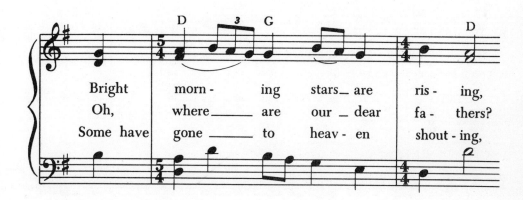

Bright morn - ing stars are ris - ing,
Oh, where are our dear fa - thers?
Some have gone to heav - en shout - ing,

Bright morn - ing stars are ris - ing,
Oh, where are our dear fa - thers?
Some have gone to heav - en shout - ing,

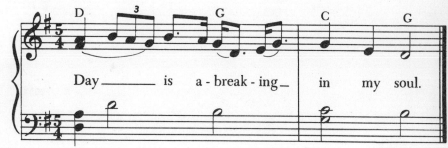

Day is a - break - ing in my soul.

4. Bright morning stars are rising,
Bright morning stars are rising,
Bright morning stars are rising,
Day is a-breaking in my soul.

5. Oh, where are our dear mothers? *etc.*

6. Some are down in the valley praying, *etc.*

7. Bright morning stars are rising, *etc.*

15

Rise Up, Shepherd, and Follow

Moderately fast (♩ = 160)

1. There's a star in the East on Christ - mas morn,
   Rise up, shep-herd, and fol - low,

2. If you take good heed to the an - gel's words,
   Rise up, shep-herd, and fol - low,

It' - ll lead to the place where the Sav - ior's born, Rise up, shep-herd, and fol - low.

You'll for - get your flocks, you'll for - get your herds,

REFRAIN

Leave your sheep and leave your lambs, Rise up, shep-herd, and fol - low,

Leave your ewes and leave your rams, Rise up, shep-herd, and fol - low.

Shepherd, Shepherd

Moderate (♩ = 88)

1. Shep - herd, shep - herd, where'd you leave your lambs?
2. Shep - herd, shep - herd, where'd you lose your sheep?

Shep - herd, shep - herd, where'd you leave your lambs?
Shep - herd, shep - herd, where'd you lose your sheep?

Shep - herd, shep - herd, where'd you leave your lambs? Oh, the
Shep - herd, shep - herd, where'd you lose your sheep? Oh, the

lambs done gone a - stray, _____ The
sheep done gone a - stray, _____ The

lambs done gone a - stray. _____
sheep done gone a - stray. _____

Don't You Hear the Lambs a-Crying?

Moderate ♩=72

TEXAS

REFRAIN

Don't you hear the lambs a-cry-ing, on the oth-er green shore?

Don't you hear the lambs a-cry-ing, O Good Shep-herd, go feed-a my sheep.

Fine

STANZA

Some for Paul and some for Si-las, Some for to make-a my heart re-joice,

D. C. without pause

Don't you hear the lambs a-cry-ing, O Good Shep-herd, go feed-a my sheep.

19

Found My Lost Sheep

Increasing one by one the number of lost sheep (and decreasing the remainder) is a natural way of adding stanzas and making this song last a long time.

Look Away to Bethlehem

Fast (♩ = 96)

1. Look, look a - way, look a - way, Look a - way to Beth - le - hem,
2. Lit - tle chil - dren, look a - way, look a - way, Look a - way-a in Beth - le - hem,

Look, look a - way, look a - way, Look a - way to Beth - le - hem.
Lit - tle chil - dren, look a - way, look a - way, Look a - way-a in Beth - le - hem.

How Many Miles to Beth-e-le-hem?

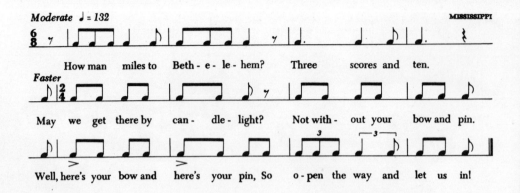

The Mississippi children who chant this game give directions for playing it. Two raise arms to make an arch, and the remainder form a line. The group chants the question, the couple answers, and the dialogue continues. At "open," the line passes under the arch and around, and under and around again and again. Among the many town-names acquired by the game over centuries of playing are Burslen, Barley Bridge, Cantelon, Dublin Town, Benjamin Town, Boston Town, Mile-a-bright—and, as in the following sung version from Maine, London Town.

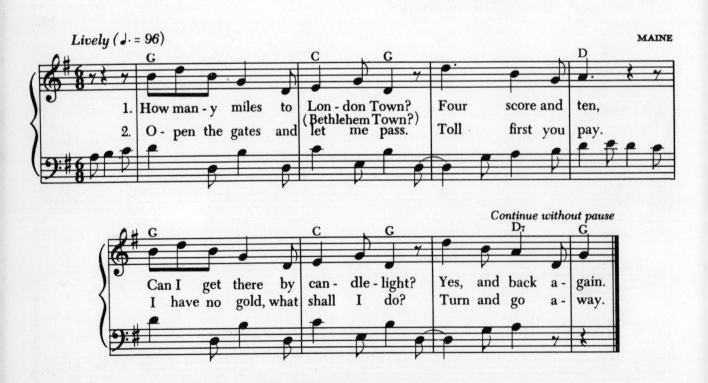

Jehovah Hallelujah

Moderate (♩ = 138)

REFRAIN

SOUTH CAROLINA

Je - ho - vah, hal - le - lu - jah, The Lord will pro - vide,

Je - ho - vah, hal - le - lu - jah, The Lord will pro - vide.

STANZA

The fox - es have a hole, and the bird - es* have a nest,

smooth

The Son of God he___ dun - no where to lay his wea - ry head.

* not birdies

23

Joseph and Mary

THE CHERRY TREE CAROL

KENTUCKY

Moderately fast ♩ = 152
PRELUDE and INTERLUDE (fiddle)

bright

Fine

STANZAS (a little slower)

smooth

1. Jo- seph was_ an old man, An_ old man was_ he,
2. As Jo- seph and Ma- ry was walk- ing, Was_ walk- ing one_ day,
3. Then Ma- ry said to Jo- seph, so_ meek and so_ mild,

D. C. for interlude after stanzas 2, 4, 6, 8 and 9

He_ mar- ried Vir- gin Ma- ry, The_ Queen of Gal- i- lee.
"Here are ap- ples, here are cher- ries," Ma- ry_ did say.
"Jo- seph gath- er me_ some cher- ries, For_ I_ am with Child."

"Bow down, cher — ry tree, Low down to — the ground."

smooth

D. C. for interlude

Ma - ry gath - ered cher - ries and — Jo - seph stood a - round.

4. Then Joseph flew in anger,
   In anger flew he,
   "Let the father of the Baby
   Gather cherries for thee."

5. Jesus spoke a few words,
   A few words spoke he,
   "Give my mother some cherries,
   Bow down, cherry tree!

6. "Bow down, cherry tree,
   Low down to the ground."
   Mary gathered cherries,
   And Joseph stood around.

7. Then Joseph took Mary
   All on his right knee,
   "What have I done, Lord?
   Have mercy on me."

8. Then Joseph took Mary
   All on his left knee,
   "Oh, tell me, little Baby,
   When Thy birthday will be."

9. "The sixth of January
   My birthday will be,
   When the stars in the elements
   Will tremble with glee."

A Virgin Most Pure

REFRAIN

Then let us be mer-ry, cast sor-rows a-way;

Our Sav-ior,— Christ Je-sus, was— born on this— day.

4. But Mary, blest Mary, so meek and so mild,
Soon wrapp-ed in swaddlings this heavenly Child.
Contented she laid Him where oxen did feed,
The great God of nature approved of the deed.

   REFRAIN:

   Then let us be merry, cast sorrows away;
   Our Savior, Christ Jesus, was born on this day.

5. Then presently after, the shepherds did spy
Vast numbers of angels to stand in the sky;
So merrily talking, so sweet did they sing:
All glory and praise to our heavenly King.
Refrain:

6. To teach us humility all this was done.
Then learn we from hence haughty pride for to shun.
A manger's His cradle who came from above,
The great God of mercy, of peace and of love.
Refrain:

Baby Born Today

MOTHER MARY, WHAT IS THE MATTER?

Moderate, somewhat free ♩ = 120

GEORGIA

1. Moth-er Ma-ry, what is the mat-ter? Oh, Je-ru-s'lem in the morn-ing.

2. Fa-ther Jo-seph, what is the mat-ter? Oh, Je-ru-s'lem in the morn-ing.

3. A ba- by born to-day,___
5. They wrapped in swad-dling clothes,
7. Born in Beth-le-hem,___
9. Je-ru-s'lem, Oh, Je-ru-s'lem,

Oh, Je-ru-s'lem in the morn-ing.

Continue without pause | Last time

4. Born___ in the man-ger,
6. Stall___ was His cra-dle,
8. Born___ in the man-ger,
10. Ba-by born to-day,___

Oh, Je-ru-s'lem in the morn-ing.

This is an old traditional "shout" sung during Christmas Eve Watch Night service. A singer begins a line, the group joins in on the refrain, another line is begun — and the song continues a long time. New lines are improvised at will, and old and new are returned to again and again in no prescribed order.

Go Tell It on the Mountain

Moderate (♩ = 120)
REFRAIN

Go tell it on the mountain, Over the hills and ev-er-y-where,

smooth

Go tell it on the mountain, That Jesus Christ is born. *Fine*

STANZA (*a little faster*)

1. In the time of David a seeker, I Some called him a King,
2. When I was a seeker, I sought both night and day,

And if a child is true born Lord Jesus will hear him sing.
I ask the Lord to help me, And He show me the way. *D. C.*

3. He made me a watchman
   Upon a city wall,
   And if I am a Christian
   I am the least of all.

Shepherds, Rejoice

Moderately fast, with determination, (♩ = 92)

1. Shep - herds, re - joice, lift up your eyes, And send your fears a - way,
2. "No gold nor pur - ple swad - dling bands, Nor roy - al shin - ing things:

News from the re - gions of the skies - "A Sav - ior's born to - day!
A man - ger for His cra - dle stands, And holds the King of Kings.

Je - sus, the God whom an - gels fear, Comes down to dwell with you!
Go, shep - herds, where the In - fant lies, And see His hum - ble throne.

To - day He makes His en - trance here, But not as mon - archs do.
With tears of joy in all your eyes, Go, shep - herds, kiss the Son."

3. Thus Gabriel sang, and straight around
   The heavenly armies throng;
   They tune their harps to lofty sound,
   And thus conclude the song:
   "Glory to God that reigns above,
   Let peace surround the earth;
   Mortals shall know their Maker's love
   At their Redeemer's birth."

4. Lord! and shall angels have their songs,
   And men no tunes to raise?
   Oh, may we lose our useless tongues,
   When they forget to praise.
   Glory to God that reigns above,
   That pitied us forlorn.
   We join to sing our Maker's love,
   For there's a Savior born.

Shepherds in Judea

Moderately fast (♩ = 69)

1. Then God sent an an- gel from heav- en so high, To
2. "A to- ken I leave you where- by you may find This

cer- tain poor shep- herds in fields where they lie, And
heav- en- ly Stran- ger, this friend to man- kind: A

bade them no long- er in sor- row to stay, Be-
man- ger His cra- dle, a stall His a- bode, The

cause__ that our Sav- ior was born__ on this day:
ox- en are near__ Him and blow on your God.

REFRAIN (♩.= ♩.= 69)

"Dis- pel all your sor- rows and ban- ish your fears, For__
Then, shep- herds, be tran- quil, this in- stant a- rise, Go__

3. This wonderful story scarce reach-ed the ear
   When thousands of angels in glory appear,
   They join in the concert, and this was the theme:
   All glory to God, and good will towards men.

   REFRAIN 3:
   Then, shepherds, go join your glad voice to the choir,
   And catch a few sparks of celestial fire,
   Then, shepherds, go join your glad voice to the choir,
   And catch a few sparks of celestial fire.

4. To Bethlehem city the shepherds repaired, .
   For full confirmation of what they had heard,
   They entered the stable, with aspect so mild,
   And there they beheld the Mother and Child.

   REFRAIN 4:
   Then, shepherds, adore, we commend thee to God,
   Go worship the Son in His humble abode,
   Then, shepherds, adore, we commend thee to God,
   Go worship the Son in His humble abode.

The New-Born Baby

Not too slow (♩ = 80)

SOUTH CAROLINA

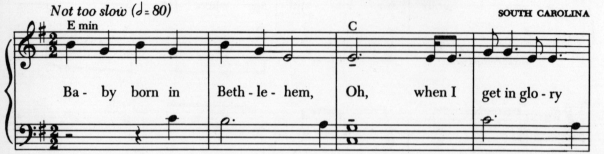

Ba - by born in Beth - le - hem, Oh, when I get in glo - ry

Oh, when I get in glo - ry, Glo - ry be to the new - born Ba - by.

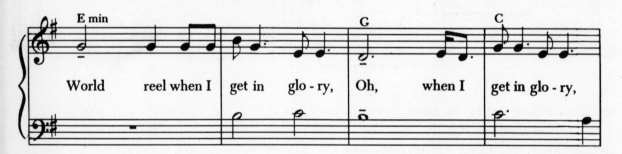

World reel when I get in glo - ry, Oh, when I get in glo - ry,

Oh, when I get in glo - ry, Glo - ry be to the new - born Ba - by.

Oh, Mary and the Baby, Sweet Lamb

Moderately fast ♩ = 120

TEXAS

SINGER I — D min — SINGER II — C — D min — SINGER I — SINGER II — C — D min

Oh, Ma - ry and the Ba - by, sweet Lamb,_ Oh, Ma - ry and the Ba - by, sweet Lamb,

SINGER I — F — D min — SINGER II — C — D min — SINGERS I and II — A min — D min

Oh, Ma - ry and the Ba - by, sweet Lamb,_ Oh, Ma - ry and the Ba - by, sweet Lamb.

2. It's a holy Baby, sweet Lamb,
   It's a holy Baby, sweet Lamb,
   It's a holy Baby, sweet Lamb,
   Oh, Mary and the Baby, sweet Lamb.

3. I love that Baby, sweet Lamb, (3)
   Oh, Mary and the Baby, sweet Lamb.

4. Oh, Mary and the Baby, sweet Lamb. (4)

5. It's a God-sent Baby, sweet Lamb, (3)
   Oh, Mary and the Baby, sweet Lamb.

6. Oh, Mary and the Baby, sweet Lamb. (4)

Star in the East

Moderately fast, *not dragging* (♩ = 108)

1. Hail the blest morn, see the great Me-di-a- tor
2. Cold on His cra- dle the dew- drops are shin- ing,

Down from the re- gions of glo- ry de- scend.
Low lies His bed, with the beasts of the stall.

Shep- herds, go wor- ship the Babe in the man- ger,
An- gels a- dore Him, in slum- bers re- clin- ing,

Lo, for His guard the bright an- gels at- tend.
Wise men and shep- herds be- fore Him do fall.

REFRAIN

Bright-est and best of the sons of the morn-ing,

Dawn on our dark-ness and lend us thine aid,

Star in the East, the ho-ri-zon a-dorn-ing,

Guide where our in-fant Re-deem-er was laid.

3. Say, shall we yield Him, in costly devotion,
Odors of Eden and offerings divine,
Gems from the mountain and pearls from the ocean,
Myrrh from the forest and gold from the mine?

REFRAIN:
Brightest and best of the stars of the morning!
Dawn on our darkness and lend us thine aid.
Star in the east, the horizon adorning,
Guide where our infant Redeemer was laid.

4. Vainly we offer each ample oblation,
Vainly with gold we His favor secure,
Richer by far is the heart's adoration,
Dearer to God are the prayers of the poor.
Refrain:

Babe of Bethlehem

3. His parents poor in earthly store
   To entertain the stranger
   They found no bed to lay His head,
   But in the ox's manger:
   No royal things, as used by kings,
   Were seen by those that found Him,
   But in the hay the stranger lay,
    With swaddling bands around Him.

4. On the same night a glorious light
   To shepherds there appeared.
   Bright angels came in shining flame,
   They saw and greatly feared.
   The angels said, "Be not afraid,
   Although we much alarm you,
   We do appear good news to bear,
   As now we will inform you.

5. "The city's name is Bethlehem,
   In which God hath appointed,
   This glorious morn a Savior's born,
   For Him God hath anointed;
   By this you'll know, if you will go,
   To see this little stranger,
   His lovely charms in Mary's arms,
   Both lying in a manger."

6. When this was said, straightway was made
   A glorious sound from heaven,
   Each flaming tongue an anthem sung,
   "To men a Savior's given,
   In Jesus' name, the glorious theme
   We elevate our voices,
   At Jesus' birth be peace on earth,
   Meanwhile all heaven rejoices."

7. Then with delight they took their flight,
   And wing'd their way to glory,
   The shepherds gazed and were amazed,
   To hear the pleasing story;
   To Bethlehem they quickly came,
   The glorious news to carry,
   And in the stall they found them all,
   Joseph, the Babe, and Mary.

8. The shepherds then return'd again
   To their own habitation
   With joy of heart they did depart,
   Now they have found salvation.
   Glory, they cry, to God on high,
   Who sent His Son to save us
   This glorious morn the Savior's born,
   His name it is Christ Jesus.

Child of God

THE LITTLE CRADLE ROCKS TONIGHT IN GLORY

Moderately fast (♩ = 72)

LOUISIANA AND GEORGIA

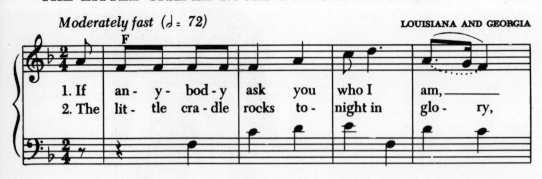

1. If an - y - bod - y ask you who I am,____
2. The lit - tle cra - dle rocks to - night in glo - ry,

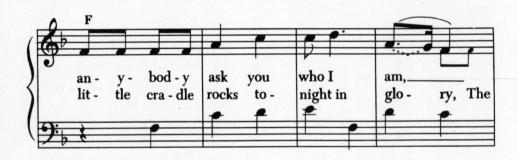

Who I am,____ who I am,____ If
In glo - ry, in glo - ry, The

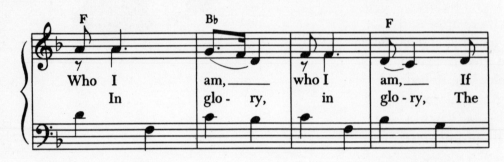

an - y - bod - y ask you who I am,____
lit - tle cra - dle rocks to - night in glo - ry, The

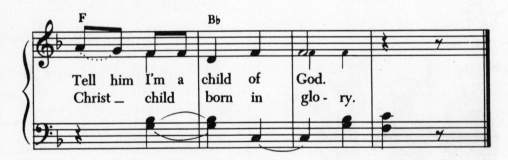

Tell him I'm a child of God.
Christ __ child born in glo - ry.

3. Peace on earth, Mary rock the cradle,
   Mary rock the cradle, Mary rock the cradle,
   Peace on earth, Mary rock the cradle,
   The Christ child born in glory.

4. The Christ child passing, singing softly,
   Singing softly, singing softly,
   The Christ child passing, singing softly,
   The Christ child born in glory.

5. Don't you hear the foot on the tree top,
   Foot on the tree top, foot on the tree top,
   Don't you hear the foot on the tree top,
   Soft like the south wind blow?

Cradle Hymn

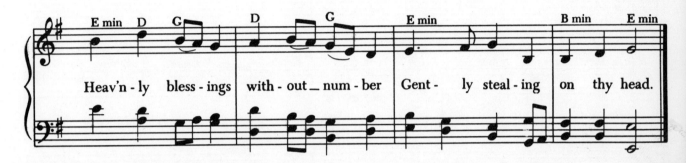

2. How much better art thou attended
   Than the Son of God could be
   When from heaven he descended
   And became a child like thee.

3. Soft and easy is thy cradle,
   Coarse and hard the Savior lay
   When His birthplace was a stable
   And His softest bed was hay.

41

Ain't That a Rocking All Night

Moderately slow (♩ = 54)

SOUTH CAROLINA

Mary had the little Baby, Born in Bethlehem,

Every time the Baby cry, She rock in a weary land.

REFRAIN

Ain't that a rocking all night, Ain't that a rocking all night,

Ain't that a rocking all night, All night long.

Sing-a-Lamb

TEXAS AND LOUISIANA

In this chant-like song the one-line stanzas may be sung in any order, and more can be improvised. Usually two or three are sung between refrains. The reiterated *sing-a-lamb* may be sung by a group.

Mary, What You Going to Na[me]

Moderate (♩ = 96)

Refrain: The Virgin Mary had-a one Son,
Stanza: If you follow that star you'll surely find a Baby,

M-m-m, Glory hallelujah,
M-m-m, Surely find a Baby,

M-m-m, Glory hallelujah,
M-m-m, Surely find a Baby,

Glory be to the new-born King.
Glory be to the new-born King.

smooth

hat Pretty Little Baby?

REFRAIN (*occasional*)
The Virgin Mary had-a one Son,
M-m-m, Glory hallelujah,
M-m-m, Glory hallelujah,
Glory be to the new-born King.

2. Mary, what you going to name that pretty little Baby?
M-m-m, pretty little Baby,
M-m-m, pretty little Baby,
Glory be to your new-born King.

3. Some call Him one thing, I think I'll call Him Jesus, *etc.*

4. Mary, what you going to name that pretty little Baby? *etc.*

5. Some call Him Jesus, I think I'll call Him Emmanuel, *etc.*

45

Sing Hallelu

Moderately fast (♩ = 120)

SOUTH CAROLINA

1. Down in a val - ley,
2. Mary had a Ba - by,
3. What did she name Him?
Sing hal - le - lu,

Down in a val - ley,
Mary had a Ba - by,
What did she name Him?
Sing hal - le - lu,

Down in a val - ley,
Mary had a Ba - by,
What did she name Him?
Sing hal - le - lu,____

Continue without pause

Down in a val - ley,
Mary had a Ba - by,
What did she name Him?
Sing hal - le - lu.

4. Named Him Jesus, Sing hallelu. (4)
   (*other stanzas give other names* —
   Prince of Peace, Mighty Counselor,
   Mighty God, Everlasting Father)

5. Where was He born? Sing hallelu. (4)

6. Born in a stable, Sing hallelu. (4)

This song can become as long as singers wish to make it. It was [ca]rried on as follows by one group of children:

7. Where did she lay Him?
8. Laid Him in a manger.
9. Who came to see Him?
10. Shepherds came to see Him.
11. Wise men brought Him presents.
12. King Herod tried to find Him.
13. They went away to Egypt.
14. Mary rode the donkey.
15. Joseph walked beside them.
16. Angels watching over.

Mary Had a Baby

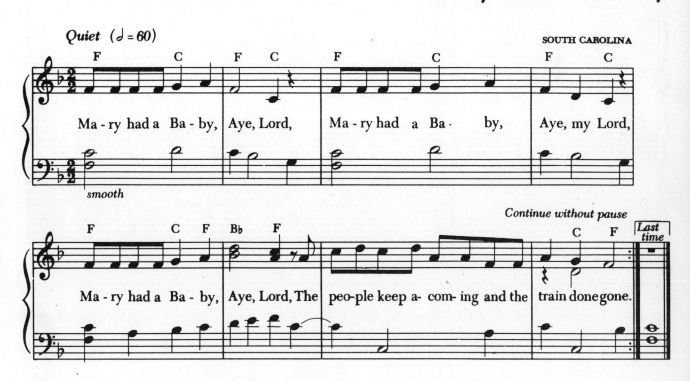

Quiet (♩ = 60)

SOUTH CAROLINA

Ma-ry had a Ba-by, Aye, Lord, Ma-ry had a Ba-by, Aye, my Lord,

smooth

Ma-ry had a Ba-by, Aye, Lord, The peo-ple keep a-com-ing and the train done gone.

Continue without pause

The stanzas of Mary Had a Baby *and* Sing Hallelu *are the same.*

47

Jesus Borned in Bethlea

Moderately slow ♩ = 72

VIRGINIA

Children have improvised many more stanzas from their knowledge of the Christmas story.

Wasn't That a Mighty Day

SOUTH CAROLINA AND TENNESSEE

Moderately fast (♩ = 100)

Was-n't that a might - y day, Hal - le - lu, __ hal - le - lu, __

Was - n't that a might - y day, When Je - sus Christ was born.

STANZA

Well, Je - sus was a ba - by, A - ly - ing at Ma - ry's arm,

Ly - ing in the sta - ble of Beth - le - hem, __ The beasts they keep-a him warm.

January, February

THE LAST MONTH OF THE YEAR

Moderately fast ♩ = 120

MISSISSIPPI

LEADER (C) GROUP

What month was my Je - sus borned in?— On the last month of the year.—

LEADER (C) GROUP

What month was my Je - sus borned in?— On the last month of the year. (Oh.)

50

As in Holy Babe (page 70), the rhythmic beat in this song is especially strong, and the rests are as important as tones. The song can be sung in any of three ways: antiphonally, by leader and group; as one continuous melody, by a single person or group; as tune and descant, by two or more persons. In the latter case, beginning at measure 5 of the refrain, the bass part should be sung as the descant above the tune — two octaves higher than written.

Poor Little Jesus

Moderate (♩ = 76)

1. It was poor ___ lit - tle Je - sus, } Yes, yes, ___
2. Poor ___ lit - tle Je - sus } Yes, yes, ___
3. Poor ___ lit - tle Je - sus,

He was born ___ on ___ Christ - mas, } Yes, yes, ___
Child ___ of ___ Ma - ry,
They ___ took Him from a man - ger,

And ___ laid ___ in a man - ger, } Yes, yes, ___
Did - n't have ___ no ___ cra - dle,
They ___ took Him from His moth - er,

Was - n't that a pit - y and a shame? Lawd, ___ Lawd,

Was - n't that a pit - y and a shame?

Heard from Heaven Today

SOUTH CAROLINA

Moderate (♩ = 84)
REFRAIN

Hur - ry on, my wea - ry soul, And I heard-a from heav - en to - day,

Hur - ry on, O my wea - ry soul, And I heard-a from heav - en to - day.

STANZA

A Ba - by born in Beth - le - hem, And I heard-a from heav - en to - day,

A Ba - by born in Beth - le - hem, And I heard-a from heav - en to - day.

D. C. without pause

ALTERNATE REFRAIN:

Travel on, my weary soul,
And I heard-a from heaven today,
Travel on, O my weary soul,
And I heard-a from heaven today.

2. The bell is a-ringing in the other bright world,
And I heard-a from heaven today,
The bell is a-ringing in the other bright world,
And I heard-a from heaven today.
Refrain:

3. The trumpet sounds in the other bright land, *etc.*

'Twas a Wonder in Heaven

Moderately fast (♩ = 84)   ALABAMA

O Lord, I won-der, Bye and bye,__

O Lord, I won-der, Bye and bye,__

Continue without pause

O Lord, I won-der, Bye and bye.

2. 'Twas a wonder in heaven, Bye and bye,
   'Twas a wonder in heaven, Bye and bye,
   'Twas a wonder in heaven, Bye and bye.

3. Oh, God told Joseph, Bye and bye. (3)

4. To take Mary and the Baby, Bye and bye. (3)

5. And go down in Egypt, Bye and bye.

6. Till Herod is dead, Bye and bye.

7. When Herod was dead, Bye and bye.

8. Oh, out of Egypt, Bye and bye.

9. Have I called my son, Bye and bye.

10. O Lord, I wonder, Bye and 'bye.

Many songs have their beginning as part of a group experience. One singer leads off with a line which comes to him at the moment, and the group — perhaps only a few at the beginning — sings a word or phrase of comment. The first singer, or perhaps another, then adds a second line, and the group again interpolates its refrain. In this manner the song grows.

Mariner's Hymn

Vigorous ($\quarternote$ = 88)

"Hail you! and where did you come from?" Hal - le - lu - jah.

"Oh, I'm come from the land of E - gypt," Hal - le - lu - jah.

2. Hail you! and where are you bound for? Hallelujah. (2)
   Oh, I'm bound for the land of Canaan, Hallelujah. (2)

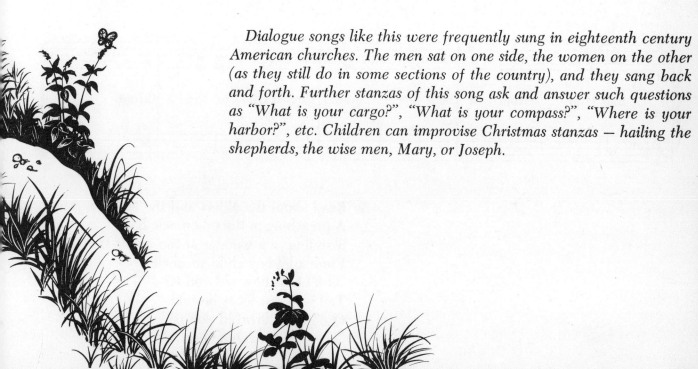

Dialogue songs like this were frequently sung in eighteenth century American churches. The men sat on one side, the women on the other (as they still do in some sections of the country), and they sang back and forth. Further stanzas of this song ask and answer such questions as "What is your cargo?", "What is your compass?", "Where is your harbor?", etc. Children can improvise Christmas stanzas — hailing the shepherds, the wise men, Mary, or Joseph.

O Mary, Where Is Your Baby?

Not dragging (♩ = 72)

LOUISIANA

1. Read in the gos-pel of Math-a-yew, The gos-pel of Luke and John,
Read a-bout Ma-ry and Jo-seph come, A-rid-ing on a don-key from far,

Read in the gos-pel and learn the news How the l'il boy Child was born.
Slept in a sta-ble of Beth-le-hem Where the shep-herds all seen the star.

REFRAIN

O_____ Ma - ry, Where is your Ba - by? They done took Him from a man - ger And carried Him to the throne.

2. Read about the elders and the Hebrew priest,
A-preaching in the tabernacle hall;
Standing in a wonder at the words they heard
From a li'l boy child so small.
"O li'l boy, how old you is?
Tell it if you let it be told.
O li'l boy, how old you is?"
"I ain't but twelve years old."

Yonder Comes Sister Mary

LOUISIANA

*The small note C may be sung instead of F, if desired.

The Blessings of Mary

Quiet (♩ = 72)

NORTH CAROLINA

smooth

The ver-y first bless-ing Ma-ry had, she had the bless-ing of one, To think that her son Je-sus was God's e-ter-nal Son, Was God's e-ter-nal Son like the Man-u-el in glo-ry,

Continue without pause

Last-time

Fa-ther, Son and the Ho-ly Ghost through all e-ter-ni-ty.

2. The very next blessing Mary had, she had the blessing of two,
To think that her son Jesus could read the Scriptures through,
Could read the Scriptures through like the Manuel in glory,
Father, Son and the Holy Ghost through all eternity.

58

3. The very next blessing Mary had, she had the blessing of three,
To think that her son Jesus could set the prisoners free, *etc*.

4. The very next blessing Mary had, she had the blessing of four,
To think that her son Jesus could live forevermore, *etc*.

5. The very next blessing Mary had, she had the blessing of five,
To think that her son Jesus could bring the dead to 'live.

6. The very next blessing Mary had, she had the blessing of six,
To think that her son Jesus could heal and cure the sick.

7. The very next blessing Mary had, she had the blessing of seven,
To think that her son Jesus could carry the keys to heaven.

8. The very next blessing Mary had, she had the blessing of eight,
To think that her son Jesus could make the crooked straight.

9. The very next blessing Mary had, she had the blessing of nine,
To think that her son Jesus could turn the water to wine.

10. The very next blessing Mary had, she had the blessing of ten,
To think that her son Jesus could write without a pen.

11. The very next blessing Mary had, she had the blessing of eleven,
To think that her son Jesus could turn the world to heaven.

12. The very next blessing Mary had, it was the blessing of twelve,
To think that her son Jesus could turn the sick to well.

Awake

3. Glory to God that reigns above, Halle, hallelujah,
   We join to sing our Maker's love, Halle, hallelujah,
   Let peace and love on earth abound, Halle, hallelujah,
   While time revolves and years roll round, Halle, hallelujah.

60

Exultation

Moderately fast (♩=138)

E min   B min   E min

1. Come a - way to the skies,__ my be - lov - ed, a - rise,
2. Now with sing - ing and praise__ let us spend all our days,

E min   B min

And re - joice in the day__ thou wast born,
By our heav - en - ly Fa - ther be - stowed,

A min   G   E min

On this fes - ti - val day come ex - ult - ing a - way,
While His grace we re - ceive from His boun - ty, And live

A min   B min   E min

And with sing - ing to Zi - on re - turn.
to the hon - or and glo - ry of God.

Children of the Heavenly King

Fast (♩ = 144)

Chil - dren of_ the heav'n - ly_ King, as we jour - ney_ let us_ sing,

Sing our_ Sav - ior's wor - thy_ praise, glo - rious in His_ works and_ ways.

We are trav-'ling home to God in the way our fa-thers trod,

They are_ hap-py now,_and_ we soon their hap-pi-ness shall see.

Singing in the Land

Moderately fast (♩ = 120)

ALABAMA

Sing - ing in the land,— Sing - ing in the land, Sing - ing in the land, I'm a
long ways from home, Sing - ing in the land,— Sing - ing in the land,

REFRAIN

Ba - by of Beth - e - le - hem. O___ sis - ter, don't you want to go to
heav - en? O___ sis - ter, don't you want to go to heav - en? O___
sis - ter, don't you want to go to heav - en? Ba - by of Beth - e - le - hem.

*No breath: let the voice carry on into the refrain

"Singing" becomes "praying," "mourning," "preaching," "shouting,"
in later stanzas, and refrains include other members of the family —
brother, father, and so on.

Rejoice My Friends

Fast (♩ = 100)

Re - joice my friends, the Lord is King! Let all___ pre - pare to take Him in.

Let Ja - cob rise and Zi - on sing, And all the earth with prais - es ring,

And give to Him the glo - ry.

2. Oh, may the desert land rejoice,
   And mourners hear the Savior's voice,
   While praise their every tongue employs,
   And all obtain immortal joys,
   And give to Him the glory.

   3. Come, parents, children, bond and free,
      Come, who will go along with me?
      I'm bound fair Canaan's land to see,
      And shout with saints eternally,
      And give to Him the glory.

   4. Those beauteous fields of living green
      By faith my joyful eyes have seen,
      Though Jordan's billows roll between,
      We soon shall cross the narrow stream,
      And give to Him the glory.

The Twelve Apostles

A CUMULATIVE SONG

Some say that each line of this very old number-song (known in other versions as Green Grow the Rushes-o, The Dilly Song, The Carol of the Numbers) *once had religious significance. Such an apparently nonsensical expression as "pot waters," for instance, may have had reference to the miracle of turning the six water pots into wine at the marriage in Cana. "Gabbling rangers" is undoubtedly related to the "Gabriel angels" or "Great Archangel" of other versions. "Nine bright shiners" ("nine of the bridal shine" in an earlier singing) referred perhaps to the nine orders of angels supposed to be present at the marriage of the Lamb. "Thrivers" is heard elsewhere as "shrivers," "riders," occasionally "strangers" (the three wise men?) "Lily-white bud" is more often "lily-white babes" (Christ and John the Baptist?). The religious significance of the number One usually remains undimmed, except for occasional confusing of "ever" and "never."*

Three versions of the song are included. The Twelve Apostles is closest to English tradition — though its singer, a Texan, learned it as a small child from her father, Illinois-born and Kansas-bred, who himself learned it as a boy on a buffalo hunt in Kansas, from a Kentuckian. Little Bitty Baby (page 69) is a fairly simple variant of the distinctly American Holy Babe (page 70).

In all three songs, stanzas are sung in the order: 1; 2 and 1; 3,2, and 1; 4,3,2, and 1; 5,4,3,2, and 1; and so on.

In The Twelve Apostles, *the dialogue "Stay and I'll sing!" etc. is spoken before singing each new stanza.*

①
Singer: Stay and I'll sing!
Group: What'll you sing?
Singer: I'll sing One.
Group: What is One?
Singer: (*sings*)

Moderately fast ♩ = 112   KANSAS

One's a One and all a-lone and that shall nev-er be-uh.

First time to ②, *second time to* ③, *etc.*

②
S: Stay and I'll sing
G: What'll you sing?
S: I'll sing Two.
G: What is Two?
S: (*sings*)

Two bear a lil-y white bud and they were clad in green, Oh,

(Go back to 1 above without pause)

66

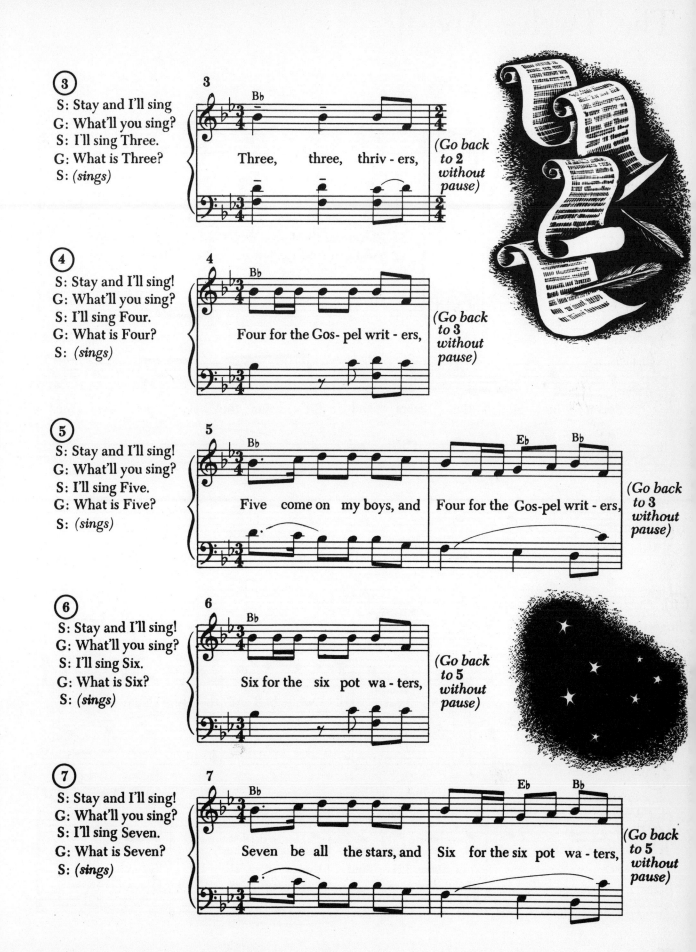

3
S: Stay and I'll sing
G: What'll you sing?
S: I'll sing Three.
G: What is Three?
S: (sings)

Three, three, thriv-ers,

(Go back to 2 without pause)

4
S: Stay and I'll sing!
G: What'll you sing?
S: I'll sing Four.
G: What is Four?
S: (sings)

Four for the Gos-pel writ-ers,

(Go back to 3 without pause)

5
S: Stay and I'll sing!
G: What'll you sing?
S: I'll sing Five.
G: What is Five?
S: (sings)

Five come on my boys, and | Four for the Gos-pel writ-ers,

(Go back to 3 without pause)

6
S: Stay and I'll sing!
G: What'll you sing?
S: I'll sing Six.
G: What is Six?
S: (sings)

Six for the six pot wa-ters,

(Go back to 5 without pause)

7
S: Stay and I'll sing!
G: What'll you sing?
S: I'll sing Seven.
G: What is Seven?
S: (sings)

Seven be all the stars, and | Six for the six pot wa-ters,

(Go back to 5 without pause)

67

Little Bitty Baby

A CUMULATIVE SONG

KENTUCKY

Holy Babe

A CUMULATIVE SONG

Moderately fast ♩ = 96 *increasing to* ♩ = 112

STANZAS 1 - 12

ARKANSAS

①-⑫ Chil - dren, go, and I will send thee. Where shall I send thee? Lord,
(will send thee)

① I shall send thee one by one, Well 1 one was the Ho - ly Ba - by, Was (to ◆)
② I shall send thee two by two, Well 2 two was the Paul and Si - las, And (to 1)
③ I shall send thee three by three, Well 3 three was the He - brew chil - dren, And (to 2)

④ I shall send thee four by four, Well 4 four was the four come a-knock-ing at the door, And (to 3)

⑤ I shall send thee five by five, Well 5 five was the Gos - pel writ - ers, And (to 4)
⑥ I shall send thee six by six, Well 6 six was the six that could-n't get fixed, And (to 5)
⑦ I shall send thee seven by seven, Well 7 sev-en was the seven came down from heav'n, And (to 6)

⑧ I shall send thee eight by eight, Well 8 eight was the eight that stood at the gate, And (to 7)

⑨ I shall send thee nine by nine, Well 9 nine was the nine that dressed so fine, And (to 8)

⑩ I shall send thee ten by ten, Well 10 ten was the Ten Com - mand - ments, And (to 9)
⑪ I shall send thee eleven by eleven, Well 11 eleven was the 'leven de - rid - ers, And (to 10)
⑫ I shall send thee twelve by twelve, Well 12 twelve was the Twelve Dis - ci - ples, And (to 11)

born by the Vir - gin   Ma - ry,__ Was   wrapped in the hol - low of   the   claw - horn, Was

D. C. without pause, for succeeding stanzas

laid   in the hol - low   of   a   man - ger, Was born,   born, Lord - y, born in   Beth - le - hem.__

This song is not so difficult as it looks. After the first three or four stanzas its strong rhythmic pulse carries it along, and the quarter rests are felt as keenly as though they were clapped or sung. The arrangement follows the original recording, which is sung in two parts. However, one singer (or group in unison) can sing the song by reading the large notes only. Holy Babe, like January, February; Baby Born Today, and similar songs, is better suited to singing than to playing on an instrument, and to group rather than to solo singing.

The Twelve Days of Christmas

A CUMULATIVE SONG

Moderate ♩ = 112
STANZAS 1 - 12

FLORIDA

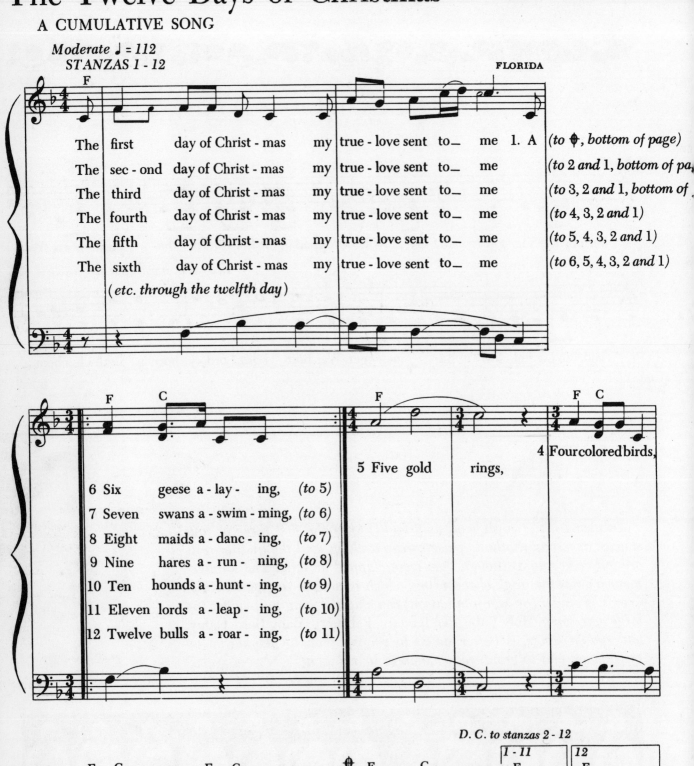

The first day of Christ - mas my true - love sent to me 1. A *(to ♦, bottom of page)*

The sec - ond day of Christ - mas my true - love sent to me *(to 2 and 1, bottom of pa...)*

The third day of Christ - mas my true - love sent to me *(to 3, 2 and 1, bottom of ...)*

The fourth day of Christ - mas my true - love sent to me *(to 4, 3, 2 and 1)*

The fifth day of Christ - mas my true - love sent to me *(to 5, 4, 3, 2 and 1)*

The sixth day of Christ - mas my true - love sent to me *(to 6, 5, 4, 3, 2 and 1)*

(etc. through the twelfth day)

5 Five gold rings,

4 Four colored birds,

6 Six geese a - lay - ing, *(to 5)*

7 Seven swans a - swim - ming, *(to 6)*

8 Eight maids a - danc - ing, *(to 7)*

9 Nine hares a - run - ning, *(to 8)*

10 Ten hounds a - hunt - ing, *(to 9)*

11 Eleven lords a - leap - ing, *(to 10)*

12 Twelve bulls a - roar - ing, *(to 11)*

D. C. to stanzas 2 - 12

1 - 11

12

3 Three French hens,

2 Two tur - tle doves,

1 A par - tridge on a pear tree.

tree.

American versions of this song show little resemblance to the English version which has become so well known during the past decade. In learning a new version of any folk song, it should be remembered that at first the new may appear less attractive than the old and familiar. With further familiarity, however, the new gradually acquires character of its own. Eventually it may either stand alongside the old, or itself become a favorite.

Over its several hundred years of singing, The Twelve Days of Christmas has often been used as a forfeit game. A leader sings the music of the first day, and each person in the group then sings the same alone, in turn. The leader sings the second day followed by the first (2 and 1, with no break in the music), and again each person sings the same alone, in turn. The third day follows in like manner (3,2, and 1) — and so on, up to twelve. Those who forget or make mistakes pay forfeit.

The Angel Band

Lively (♩ = 72)

SOUTH CAROLINA

1. There was one, there was two, there was three little an - gels,
There was four, there was five, there was six little an - gels,
There was seven, there was eight, there was nine little an - gels,

Ten lit - tle __ an - gels in the band.

Stanzas often continue on up to a hundred, ten at a time, with variations such as "There's eleven little, twelve little, thirteen little angels," or "Twenty-one, twenty-two, twenty-three little angels." Christmas refrains can be improvised — "Wasn't that a band on Christmas morning," "Jesus born on a Friday morning," and so on.

Almost Day

LOOKA DAY

LOUISIANA

Moderately fast ♩ = 120

Refrain: Chick - en crowing_ for mid - night, And it's al - most _ day,
Stanza: Thought I heard_ my moth-er say,_ It's al - most _ day,

Continue without pause

Chick - en crowing_ for mid - night, And it's al - most_ day.
Thought I heard_ my moth-er say,_ It's al - most_ day.

Still in many out-of-the-way places it is said that at midnight on Christmas Eve cocks crow to announce the holy hour, and animals talk and bow their heads in prayer. At a South Carolina Watch Night service it was the rooster's crowing that changed the Christmas singing in spirit and speed from solemnity to rejoicing. And at a similar service in Georgia a song, Looka Day, was begun at midnight and returned to again and again until the hailing of the morning star. Its tune has not been preserved, but the tune of the related song, Almost Day, can be adapted to such lines as:

1. Oh, true believer, oh, looka day. (2)
2. Day there a-coming, oh, looka day. (2)
3. Look out the window, oh, looka day. (2)
4. See day a-coming, oh, looka day. (2)

Other holiday stanzas can be improvised — about "stockings in the chimney and it's almost day," morning star a-rising, Christmas Day a-coming, turkey in the oven (on Christmas Day), and so on.

Heaven Bell Ring

SOUTH CAROLINA

Moderately fast (♩ = 80)

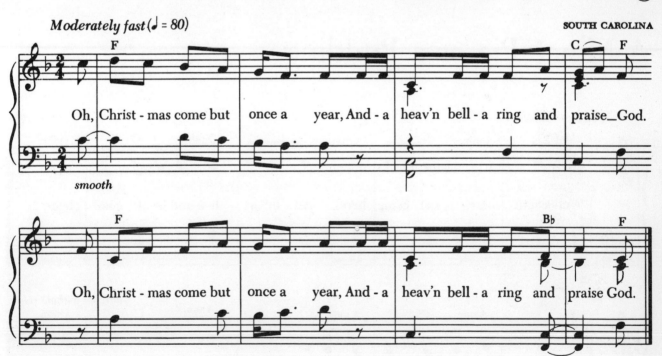

Oh, Christ-mas come but once a year, And-a heav'n bell-a ring and praise_God.

smooth

Oh, Christ-mas come but once a year, And-a heav'n bell-a ring and praise God.

2. My Lord, my Lord, what shall I do?
   And-a heaven bell-a ring and praise God.
   My Lord, my Lord, what shall I do?
   And-a heaven bell-a ring and praise God.

3. You look to the Lord with a tender heart, *etc.*

A Mince Pie or a Pudding

Moderately fast (♩ = 104)

NEW YORK

Wel - come here, wel - come here, All be a - live and be of good cheer,

Continue without pause

I've got a pie all baked com - plete,— Pud - ding, too, that's ver - y sweet.

This is one of many "welcome" songs used in Shaker communities to greet friends, especially elders or ministers.

Christmas Day in the Morning

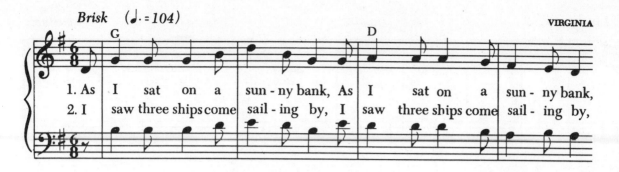

Brisk (♩.=104)

VIRGINIA

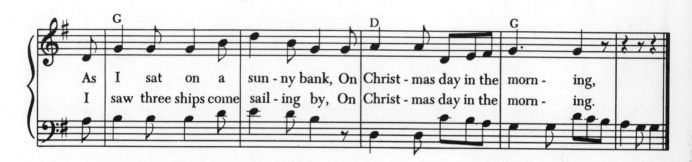

1. As I sat on a sun-ny bank, As I sat on a sun-ny bank,
2. I saw three ships come sail-ing by, I saw three ships come sail-ing by,

As I sat on a sun-ny bank, On Christ-mas day in the morn-ing,
I saw three ships come sail-ing by, On Christ-mas day in the morn-ing.

3. And who do you think was in those three ships, (3)
   But Joseph and his fair lady.

4. Then he did whistle and she did sing, (3)
   On Christmas Day in the morning.

5. And all the bells on earth did ring.

6. And all the angels in heaven did sing.

7. For the joy of the new-born King.

8. Then let us all rejoice again.

The following stanzas were heard on the streets of New York in 1880:

1. I wash my face in a golden vase,
   A golden vase, a golden vase,
   I wash my face in a golden vase
   Upon a Christmas morning.

2. I wipe my face on a lily-white towel.

3. I comb my hair with an ivory comb.

4. Two little ships were sailing by.

5. Guess who was in one of them.

6. The blessed Virgin and her Son.

7. Guess who was in the other of them.

8. George Washington and his son.

Old Christmas

A FIDDLE TUNE

KENTUCKY

This arrangement is based on an indistinct field recording. Writing of pioneer Christmas customs in Texas, Mary Daggett Lake says: "It will never be known how much the early settlers of Texas owed to the stirring notes of the fiddle. Every home, cross-roads store and community had its fiddler, and so much a part of the man was his fiddle that they were scarcely ever seen apart."